VIOLIN

Traditional fiddle music from around the world

CHRISTMAS FIDDLER

Selected and arranged by
Edward Huws Jones

BOOSEY & HAWKES

Published by Boosey & Hawkes Music Publishers Ltd
Aldwych House
71–91 Aldwych
London
WC2B 4HN

www.boosey.com

ISMN 979-0-060-11065-8 | ISBN 978-0-85162-275-0 (complete)
ISMN 979-0-060-11066-5 | ISBN 978-0-85162-276-7 (separately sold violin part)

First impression 2022

Printed by Halstan:
Halstan UK, 2-10 Plantation Road, Amersham, Bucks, HP6 6HJ. United Kingdom
Halstan DE, Weißliliengasse 4, 55116 Mainz. Germany

All arrangements by Edward Huws Jones
Music setting by Jack Thompson

Cover design by Chloë Alexander Design
Cover image: Yaroslav Antonov

CHRISTMAS FIDDLER

Selected and arranged by
Edward Huws Jones

Preface

Christmas is a wonderful time for music! Every school, college, choir, band and church has its Christmas concert (one of the musical highlights of the year), and outside the streets are full of carol singers, brass bands and buskers in Santa hats.

Christmas fiddlers can draw on a rich and varied repertoire. This collection spans seven centuries, from the boisterous medieval *Song of the ass* to contemporary tunes like *Sleigh ride*, taking in such traditional carols as *Away in a manger* and *O little town of Bethlehem* along the way. There is music in *The Christmas Fiddler* from England, Wales, France, Germany and North America.

Of course Christmas-time is not only a religious festival. Much of the music here – the Welsh carol *Deck the hall*, the "fireside" movement from *The Four Seasons*, the modern classic *Chestnuts roasting on an open fire* – is as much a celebration of the ancient secular festival of the Winter Solstice.

The arrangements in this collection follow the same flexible format as other volumes in the series. They can be performed as solos or duets, or by larger ensembles. The keyboard accompaniments are there for a multitude of purposes, from concert performances to playing at home; and the violin accompaniments (at the end of the Complete book) will be invaluable for those Christmas busking sessions.

My thanks to the students of Selby Music Centre, North Yorkshire, who beta-tested many of the arrangements; to Vanessa for adding her own festive spin; and to Anthony Marks for his eclectic sense of the whole Christmas repertoire.

Edward Huws Jones

Préface

Noël est un moment merveilleux pour la musique ! Chaque école, université, chorale, orchestre et église a son concert de Noël (un des grands moments musicaux de l'année) et les rues s'emplissent de chants de Noël, d'orchestres d'harmonie et de musiciens portant des chapeaux de Père Noël.

Les violonistes de Noël peuvent puiser dans un répertoire riche et varié. Ce recueil couvre sept siècles, de l'entraînante chanson médiévale *Song of the ass* aux airs contemporains tel que *Sleigh ride*, en passant par des chants de Noël traditionnels tels que *Away in a manger* et *O little town of Bethlehem*. On trouvera dans *The Christmas Fiddler* des musiques venues d'Angleterre, du Pays de Galles, de France, d'Allemagne, et d'Amérique du Nord.

Away in a manger

Traditional

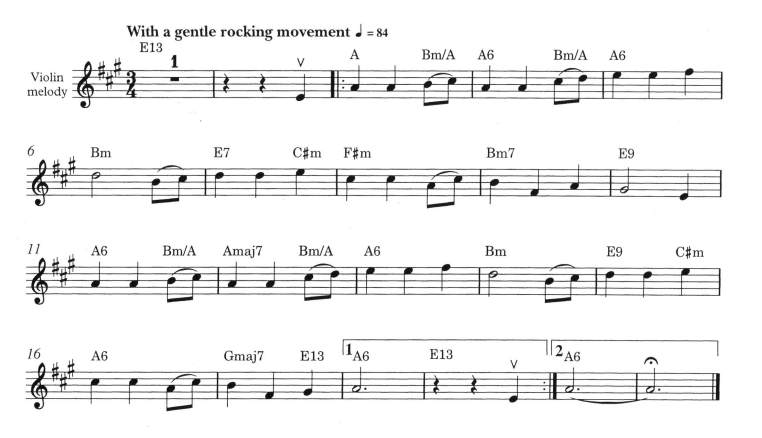

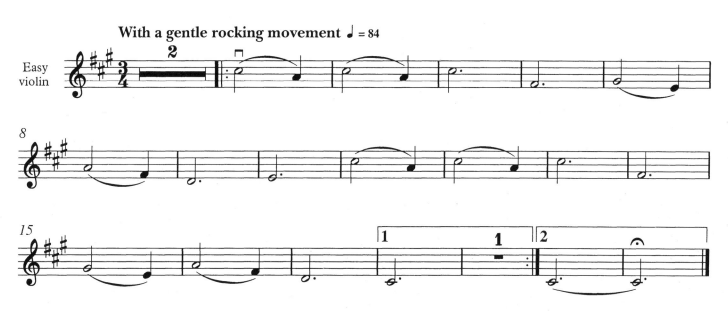

The Christmas song
(Chestnuts roasting on an open fire)

Mel Torme
& Robert Wells

Deck the hall with boughs of holly

(Nos galon)

Traditional Welsh

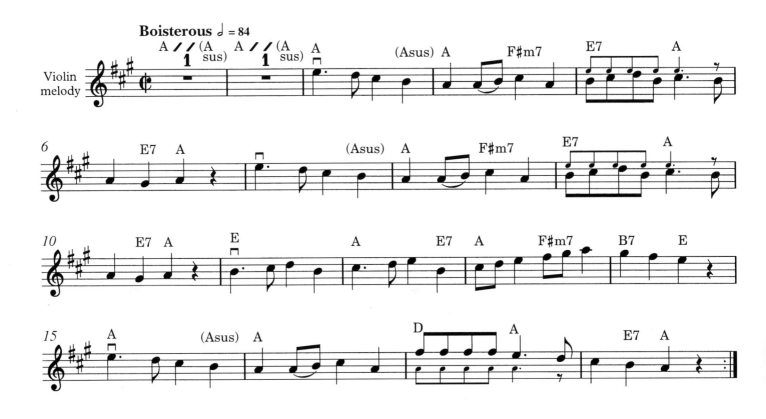

Gaudete
Rejoice!

16th century German

Good King Wenceslas

Traditional

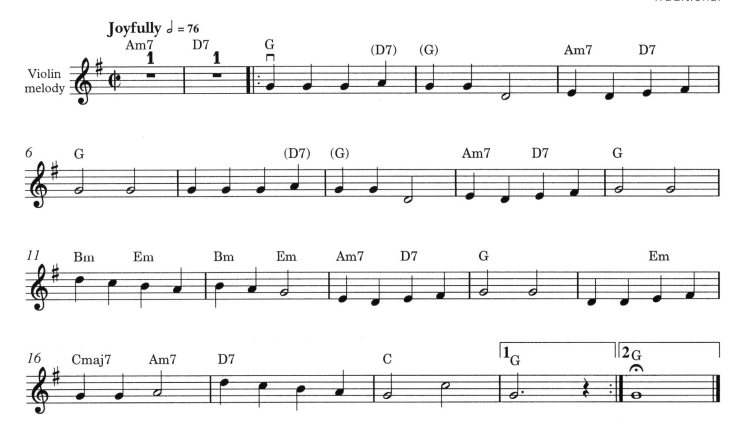

Il est né, le divin enfant

Traditional French

Jingle bells

Traditional

O little town of Bethlehem

Traditional

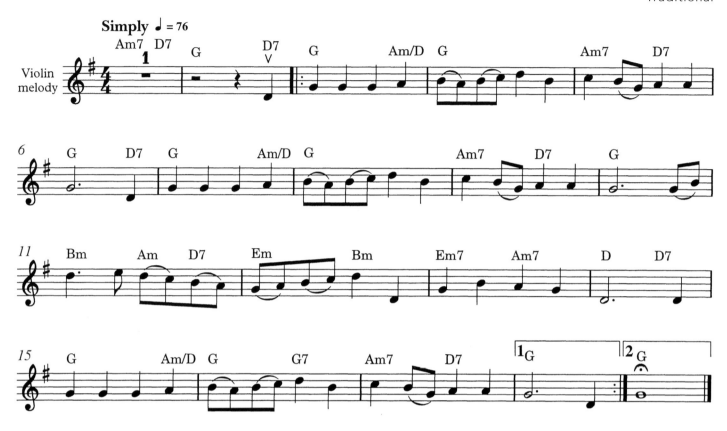

Once in royal David's city

Traditional

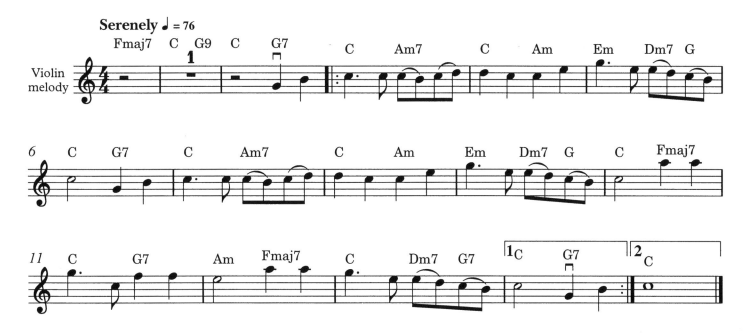

Pastoral symphony
from *Messiah*

George Frideric Handel

Silent night

Franz Gruber

Sleigh ride

Mitchell Parish
& Leroy Anderson

Song of the ass
(Orientus partibus)

13th century French

We three kings of Orient are

J H Hopkins

Winter
from *The Four Seasons*

Antonio Vivaldi